About the Author

Daksha Patel is of Indian origin. She was born in October 1975. She has a BA Honours Degree in English with History. She also has a Post Graduate Certificate in Primary Education that includes Qualified Teacher Status from Brunel University.

Daksha is fluent in Gujarati and also holds a purple belt in the martial art of karate.

Ms Patel is a published poet and her first book is called *The Modern Poetry of Daksha Patel* (ISBN 978-1-78830-142-8) under Olympia Publishers.

Daksha Patel's motto in life is that 'if at first you don't succeed in your aims and objectives then you should try, try and try again'. Education is for character building and enables us to shine like stars when we succeed at it.

Natural Knowledge Comprehension Book

Ms Daksha Patel

Natural Knowledge Comprehension Book

Olympia Publishers
London

www.olympiapublishers.com
OLYMPIA PAPERBACK EDITION

Copyright © Ms Daksha Patel 2021

The right of Ms Daksha Patel to be identified as author of
this work has been asserted in accordance with sections 77 and 78
of the Copyright, Designs and Patents Act 1988.

All Rights Reserved

No reproduction, copy or transmission of this publication
may be made without written permission.
No paragraph of this publication may be reproduced,
copied or transmitted save with the written permission of the
publisher, or in accordance with the provisions
of the Copyright Act 1956 (as amended).

Any person who commits any unauthorised act in relation to
this publication may be liable to criminal
prosecution and civil claims for damage.

A CIP catalogue record for this title is
available from the British Library.

ISBN: 978-1-78830-955-4

This is a work of fiction.
Names, characters, places and incidents originate from the writer's
imagination. Any resemblance to actual persons, living or dead, is
purely coincidental.

First Published in 2021

Olympia Publishers
Tallis House
2 Tallis Street
London
EC4Y 0AB
Printed in Great Britain

Dedication

I dedicate this book to my family, my teachers and Swami Vivekananda who is my role model.

Acknowledgements

Also, a special thank you to Anita and Ajay of Newell Glass & Locks whose funding has made this book possible.

Contents

Haiku: The Cartoon Character

The top cartoon cat,
He has a spotty bow tie.
And, wears a nice suit.

By Daksha Patel

Haiku: The Cartoon Character Poem Comprehension

1. What is this poem about?

2. What is meant by, 'The top… cat'?

3. Do you own a cat?

4. What colour eyes do cats have?

5. Do you watch cartoons?

6. What can you learn from cartoons?

7. Are Tom and Jerry cartoons teaching self-defence or just plain violence?

8. In the haiku, is the cat wearing clothes?

9. Do you like cats?

10. Are big cats dangerous?

Notes on Haiku: Cartoon Character Poem

Haiku: Churches

Churches with gargoyles,
They scare off evil spirits.
Gothic in design.

By Daksha Patel

Haiku: Churches Poem Comprehension

1. What is a church?

2. Have you been in a church?

3. What are gargoyles?

4. What is meant by ‘evil spirits’?

5. What do you associate with the word gothic?

6. What is the rule for a haiku poem?

7. How many syllables are there in total for this poem?

8. Are gargoyles scary?

9. Why are gargoyles scary?

10. What are the characteristics of gothic architecture?

Notes on Haiku: Churches Poem

Haiku: Potatoes

Crispy potatoes,
They fry slowly in the pan.
Sizzling in oil.

By Daksha Patel

Haiku: Potatoes Poem Comprehension

1. Which country do haiku poems originate from?

2. What is this poem about?

3. What is a potato?

4. Do potatoes grow under the ground?

5. Do followers of the Jain faith eat potatoes?

6. Find an adjective word in the poem.

7. Name a preposition word in the poem.

8. Name a noun in the poem.

9. What is the onomatopoeic word used in the poem?

10. Have you ever used a frying pan to cook food in?

Notes on Haiku: Potatoes Poem

Haiku: Cookies

Chocolate chip cookies,
They crumble inside your mouth.
The cookies taste sweet.

By Daksha Patel

Haiku: Cookies Poem Comprehension

1. What is a cookie?

2. Find the alliteration in the poem.

3. What word is used to describe the taste of the cookies?

4. Which line best describes the texture of the cookies?

5. Is the texture of the cookies more important than the taste?

6. The Japanese are said to 'eat with their eyes'. What does that mean?

7. What is the preposition word in the poem?

8. Have you ever baked cookies?

9. What does it mean 'to have a sweet tooth'?

10. Are cookies good for diabetics?

Notes on Haiku: Cookies Poem

Haiku: Roses

Ruby red roses,
Their petals feel velvety.
Their smell is intense.

By Daksha Patel

Haiku: Roses Poem Comprehension

1. What is this poem about?

2. Where is the alliteration in the poem?

3. What do the rose petals feel like in the poem?

4. Describe the level of smell in the poem.

5. What is the colour of the roses in the poem?

6. Can you eat roses?

7. Have you ever tasted rose syrup?

8. What can you use rose water for?

9. Have you ever eaten an Indian sweet made with rose petals?

10. What can you use rose oil for?

Notes on Haiku: Roses Poem

The Wolves

Wolves originate from the dog family.
Furry and generally grey in colour,
They run fast and have great stamina.
Wolves can reach speeds of up to 65km per hour.
They have strong will power and great leg power too.
For, they can maintain their speed for 30km before tiredness sets in.
Also, because of their diet, wolves are hardly ever skinny or thin.

Wolves are also associated with the gothic and full moon.
Their sharp teeth are made for a bloody and carnivorous diet.
And their scary howls can be heard far and wide.
Some wolves hunt at night too.
This adds to their frightening image and behaviour.
For the cubs, the adult wolves are like their saviour.

Hunting in packs of about 30 members,
The wolves go for 'strength in numbers'.
The adult wolves teach the young how to hunt in packs and survive.
And also, the wolves actually cooperate and look after each other in a friendly and loving manner.
They lick each other clean.
And, they communicate with their howls to stay together.

Especially, when hunting in the dark woods.
Just like us, they eat together as a happy family would.

The wolves are not as scary as they look.
But their reputation is really bad in story books.

By Daksha Patel

The Wolves Comprehension

1. The wolves come from the dog family. Is that true or false?

2. Why do wolves lick each other?

3. What are wolves associated with?

4. When do wolves hunt?

5. What is a carnivorous diet?

6. What is meant by ‘strength in numbers’?

7. Why does a wolf howl?

8. What is the typical colour of a wolf?

9. In ‘The Little Red Riding Hood’ story is the wolf good or bad?

10. Do wolves generally have a good reputation in stories?

Notes on The Wolves

Flower Picking

The bold white flowers are plucked for daily worship.
Their fresh fragrance spreads far.
The flower petals are unspoilt and symmetrical,
With no bugs and parasites in them,
And no half-eaten leaves or petals.
It is only after watering the flowers that they begin to settle.

The flowers have a soft and silky texture to them.
The white flowers come in a variety of shapes and sizes.
There is beauty in the strength of a flower.
There is flower power!
Thus, only the strongest flowers are selected for daily worship.
And only the pure and best ones make it into the flower vases.
The vases are filled with clean water, especially for the flowers.
And the scent coming from the flowers permeates the whole shrine room for hours and hours.

The flowers are 'beauty with a purpose'.
They act as a natural gift from nature.
Living a short life, the flowers die and wilt in the shrine room.
As the fallen petals are cleared with a broom,
We are reminded of the fact that that which lives must also die soon,

The flowers open in the sun and close under the light of the moon.

The flowers symbolise us giving our love and devotion to God.
And like the smell that fills the air,
We are reminded that God is everywhere.

By Daksha Patel

Flower Picking Comprehension

1. What is this poem about?

2. Why are the flowers described as bold?

3. What is the significance of the flowers being white?

4. Does white always symbolise purity?

5. What is purity?

6. Do you pick the strong and beautiful flowers for worship?

7. What does the flower symbolise in Hindu worship?

8. Simplify the word fragrance.

9. Do you use flowers for daily worship?

10. Have you ever purchased a fragrance from a perfume shop?

Notes on Flower Picking

Scratch Cards

Using a shiny coin to scratch off the grey coating on my colourful cards,
I am hoping that each card reveals a matching number or symbol.

By performing this ritual, I am buying into a dream of getting rich in today's life.

All I want is to win, win, win and be blessed by the goddess Laxmi.

By Daksha Patel

Scratch Cards Comprehension

1. What colour is the coating on the scratch cards?

2. What is being searched for on the scratch cards?

3. What is meant by ritual?

4. Is it natural to gamble?

5. What age do you have to be to play the scratch cards?

6. What does it mean to be blessed by the goddess, Laxmi?

7. Why do you think the word 'dream' is used in the text?

8. Do you know anyone who has won money on the scratch cards?

9. Is gambling a good thing?

10. Can gambling be addictive?

Notes on Scratch Cards

The Polar Bear

The polar bear,
He blends into his Arctic habitat of snow without fear.
For, he is one of the biggest predators there.

In the Arctic, the bear uses his size and powerful paws to hunt his prey.
He eats seals, small walruses, fish and other marine life that is spare.
He eats his fair share.

The polar bear finds the scent of the seals in their snow burrows.
He does this with the aid of his clever and sensitive nose.

He can dive and swim in cold water for long hours without gills and fins.
For, he has protective fat under his thick animal skin.
His fur is like a fluffy white duvet that you can sleep in.
Thus, sometimes polar bears are hunted for their warm and furry skin.

In the Arctic, the snow falling from the sky looks like white wedding confetti and rice.
The polar bear walks on the freezing snow and transparent ice.
He does this as easily as an expert ice-skater skating on a frozen lake.

The fishes under the ice are already wide awake.
They bunch together, ready for the take.
When the polar bear pierces the lake with his deadly paws,
It leaves us standing in awe,
As we learn that he can catch fish just with his paws.
Without a net, fishing line or bait,
There is nothing left to luck or fate.
For, he is an expert at fishing in the Arctic water or on a frozen lake.
The polar bear eats fishes as if they were cuts of meaty steak,
He uses the cold ice as his natural plate.
And sometimes, he uses his food to feed his young or to attract a suitable mate.

By Daksha Patel

The Polar Bear Comprehension

1. Where are polar bears found?

2. What do polar bears eat?

3. What makes the polar bear an expert hunter?

4. What colour is the polar bear?

5. Can polar bears swim?

6. What is the weather like in the Arctic?

7. How does a polar bear stay out of the water?

8. What is ice-skating?

9. Why don't polar bears freeze in the Arctic water?

10. Do polar bears camouflage in the snow?

Notes on The Polar Bear

The Natural Pearl

A grain of sand navigates its way into a living oyster.
Inside the shell there is moisture.
Rolling around in the shell the grain irritates the oyster from within.
The secretion inside coats the sand grain with layers like skin.
The rolling action forms a perfect spherical bead.
With a shiny coating that sparkles, the pearls are like magical seeds.
The layers created on the pearl are like those of an onion that you can eat,
Wrapped around and around in spherical sheets.
But the sheets are hard, just like the white enamel on our human teeth.

A lady wears a necklace of white pearls around her neck.
On a special occasion it brings her good luck.
But ultimately, the pearl is a gift from the ocean floor.
The pearls shimmer right up to the jeweller's door.
Inside the showroom, the lighting entices the pearls to shine more.

With their tags on, we know that the pearls have a hefty price.
But this is all for us wearing something that's personal, costly and nice.

By Daksha Patel

The Natural Pearl Comprehension

1. What does navigate mean?

2. How does the grain of sand get its pearl coating?

3. What is a spherical shape?

4. What does the inside of an oyster wall look like?

5. Where can you find oysters?

6. Why do people wear pearls?

7. Can you eat oysters?

8. Can pearls be farmed commercially?

9. Are pearls expensive?

10. Have you ever worn a pearl necklace?

Notes on The Natural Pearl

The Caterpillar

Starting with a tiny egg,
On a single green leaf shaped like a spoon,
A small caterpillar emerges out of the egg at 12:00 noon.

Eating lots of green leaves,
Until he is fat,
The caterpillar makes his own cocoon,
In which he encases himself for some time soon.

When the caterpillar emerges out of the cocoon,
He soon becomes a beautiful butterfly.
Leaving behind his old caterpillar life,
He transforms himself for a new butterfly life.
He then flies away with his light, colourful and symmetrical wings.
Thus, from caterpillar to butterfly, his new journey now begins.

By Daksha Patel

The Caterpillar Comprehension

1. What is this poem about?

2. What type of creature is a caterpillar?

3. What do caterpillars eat?

4. Why does a caterpillar eat until it is fat?

5. What does the caterpillar surround himself in?

6. What creature does the caterpillar change into?

7. Are the wings of a butterfly symmetrical?

8. Find the alliteration in the poem.

9. Why do you think a butterfly has colourful wings?

10. What patterns are common on butterfly wings?

Notes on The Caterpillar

The Desert

Vegetation is scarce in the Sahara.
The wind blows the hot sand that creates large sand dunes.
The sand dunes look like waves in an ocean.

The only plant to be found with water inside is the cactus plant.
But the cactus plant has thorns on it, making it difficult to eat.
When the camels eat the cactus plant they bleed in the mouth,
But still they do not stop eating it.

The Sahara is home to desert rats, scorpions and snakes.
They use the desert sand to hide in and keep cool from the blazing sun.

Water is pure gold in the Sahara Desert.

By Daksha Patel

The Desert Comprehension

1. What is a desert?

2. What are sand dunes?

3. Is there water in the cactus plant?

4. What makes the cactus difficult to eat?

5. Do camels eat the cactus plant?

6. What happens to the mouth of the camel eating the cactus plant?

7. Name two animals that live in the desert.

8. Why do animals hide in the sand?

9. Name one reptile.

10. What other animals can survive in the desert?

Notes on The Desert

The Cheetah

The cheetah is light in weight,
And he is evolved for speed.
The cheetah out-runs our fastest human athlete.
The cheetah runs for his meat,
So he can then eat.

The spots on him become a blur,
When he runs and reaches speeds of up to 100km per hour.
He does this without being sour.

The cheetah's retractable claws help him to grip the ground and hunt.
And thus, he out-runs his prey of antelopes, buffalos and zebras.
Also, when hunting,
The cheetah's nose can catch the smell of all the other animals around him.
In his mouth, he tastes the cool air when running like a rocket.
He feels the breeze of the wind over his furry and fashionable spotty skin.
When actually compared to a lion or tiger, the cheetah is bony and thin.

The cheetah is the fastest running animal on land.
He goes from fast, faster, to the fastest in under a minute.

When he is speeding like a sports car,
The cheetah hunts without making a sound.
Plus, his prey is also silent when it is lying dead on the ground.

To the cheetah, the prey may well be nothing more than some solid and soul-less meat,
But, do we condemn the animals for what they naturally eat?

By Daksha Patel

The Cheetah Comprehension

1. What skills of the cheetah does this text focus on?

2. Is being light in weight an advantage?

3. What is meant by the word 'evolved'?

4. Can a cheetah out-run a human being?

5. What type of claws does the cheetah have?

6. Can a cheetah out-run zebras and gazelles?

7. The cheetah is the fastest animal on land. Is this true or false?

8. What speeds can a cheetah achieve?

9. Find the superlative in the text.

10. What is an athlete?

Notes on The Cheetah

The Tiger

Camouflaged in his bold black stripes, the tiger roars.
He shows off his sharp and shiny claws.
The saliva drips from his jaw and falls on to the earthy floor.

The tiger's piercing green eyes are like daggers and knives.
As he hides behind a tree, he is covered with its falling leaves.

His eyes are hungry for food.
So there he stands in a famished mood.

The tiger then creeps up and jumps on to his living prey.
He uses his five senses to capture one animal that is alone and in fear.
For, he is also giving the others in the herd a deadly scare.

The tiger takes his prey roughly to the ground,
Biting its neck and dragging it into the dirt around and around.

The tiger crunches on the bones of his prey.
While eating his fair share,
The tiger uses his sharp canine teeth to rip apart flesh.
The carcass of the animal is bloody and fresh.
While smelling the blood,

With a rough tongue, like sandpaper, the tiger licks his tasty food.
He chews his meal as he is now in a happy mood.
For, he has hunted his own fresh food.

Although they both have stripes in common, the tiger sees the zebra only as his food.

By Daksha Patel

The Tiger Comprehension

1. Can the tiger smell blood?

2. What is meant by the phrase '(his)… eyes are like daggers'?

3. What is the purpose of the canine teeth?

4. Name the five senses.

5. Identify one simile in the text.

6. How does the tiger look upon his prey?

7. Which animal is being hunted in the text?

8. What do zebras and tigers have in common?

9. How does the tiger kill its prey?

10. Find some adjectives in the text.

Notes on The Tiger

The Apple Trees

Trees are generally blessed with a long life.
They consist of root, trunk and leaves.

The roots fix the tree to the ground,
Bringing water and nutrients all around.

The tree trunks carry the leaves high,
Up to the sunny sky.

The leaves compete for the sunlight.
And they make their own food through photosynthesis.
Although the green leaves are thin,
They still give out oxygen for us to breathe in.

In the spring season, the apple trees bud and blossom.
The flowers hanging on the trees are pastel white.
With white bunches of fragrant flowers,
The bees are busy buzzing and pollinating those flowers.
The bees are the vampires of the flower world,
For they strive hard to collect nectar from the flowers,
To make honey for the beehives in trays stacked up like towers.

When the summer comes, the trees bear its fruits of apples.
The apples are ripe and delicious for us and other animals to eat.

The smell is fresh, clean and sweet in the apple orchard.
The bruised apples are juiced, or they make it into the cider.
The trees are thick with foliage.
The branches bend with the weight of the fruits.
Summertime is for apple picking and wearing old outdoor boots.

In autumn, the apple trees shed their yellow and brown leaves,
Which fall to the ground and crumble into dry dust,
If not trodden into the muddy ground by us.

When winter arrives, the apple trees lay bare outside.
Without their green leaves, they are as naked as a human skeleton.
A mass of twigs is what we see,
In the cold frosty winter, the trees go to sleep.
Until the next season, when the whole seasonal cycle comes to repeat,
And there are apples in the orchard for everyone to eat.

By Daksha Patel

The Apple Trees Comprehension

1. Can trees be older than human beings?

2. What are the parts of a tree?

3. What is photosynthesis?

4. What are the four seasons?

5. Do trees give out oxygen?

6. Do trees give out oxygen in the day or night?

7. Which season is the apple picking season?

8. What happens to the bruised apples?

9. In what season do apple trees blossom?

10. What does the word 'foliage' mean?

Notes on The Apple Trees

The Lion Safari

In the dry African savannah,
The lion camouflages in the tall yellow grasses.
The lion is known as lord of the beasts,
And king of the jungle.
Being the big cat,
He's at the top of the food chain.

He is 'the lion king',
A symbol of royal power and prestige.

Golden in colour,
His mane is like an open dandelion flower.
And, he serves as an animal seat to the Hindu goddess Durga,
Who flashes her weapons while sitting on him in a red sari with pleats.

Lions live in families known as prides.
And, their ROARS can be heard eight kilometres far and wide.

When hunting mammals like buffalos and gazelles,
The lion out-runs its prey and catches it in a pounce,
Breaking bones and sinking its canines into the defeated animal's flesh.

The lions are strong carnivores with binocular vision.
They are predators like us.

They love red meat,
And enjoy the taste of raw blood,
Like vampires sucking on human beings.
The hunting lion drags the bleeding carcass to the pride for consumption,
So that every animal member is fed and takes part in the bloody feast.

In the African savannah,
It is the law of the jungle that counts.
For the wild animals:
It is 'the survival of the fittest' and only the strongest survive the tests of courage.

There is no place for the weak here,
Except in the jaws of death.
Every living animal seeks something to eat and feast on.
And thus, the 'circle of life' is complete.
'Who ever heard of a lion that could eat grass.'

The moral of this poem is:
Stay strong,
Even in defeat.
Be a lion and not a bleating sheep!

By Daksha Patel

The Lion Safari Comprehension

1. Where is the location of this poem set?

2. What does ‘camouflage’ mean?

3. What flower is the lion compared with?

4. Who is Durga?

5. What is the onomatopoeic word in the poem?

6. Why do you think the word ROAR is in capital letters?

7. What is a carnivore?

8. What is binocular vision?

9. What is a predator?

10. What is meant by the term, ‘the survival of the fittest’?

Notes on The Lion Safari

Glossary

Adjectives are describing (descriptive) words such as: striped, moving, furry.

Adverbs tell you how it's done, such as how someone eats, e.g. quickly.

Alliteration is the repeating of a sound, e.g. The snake slithered slowly.

Haikus: short poems from Japan — they have three lines and 17 syllables in total.

Metaphor is when you compare something to something else without using 'like' or 'as'.

Nouns are naming words such as: Daksha, Africa and door.

Onomatopoeia is a word used to make a sound, e.g. bang, click, hiss.

Personification is something that has human quality that is attached to something like an object, e.g. the black board stares and the leaves smile.

Prepositions are where we or something is situated, e.g. We are *under* the bridge.

Rhyme is when the ending of the poem has the same sound as previous lines.

Simile is when you describe something similar to something else using the words ‘like’ or ‘as’.

Superlative describes the highest degree of a quality (adjective or adverb), e.g. bravest, most beautiful.

Verbs are doing words such as jump, dive, sing.

The difference between a verse and a stanza is that verses are all equal and stanzas are chunks that are not equal.

Bibliography /Sources

Books:
Hills and Mountains by Mark C.W. Sleep, Young Explorer, pages: 17, 28.

The Illustrated Encyclopedia of Wildlife, Volume 2, pages: 76, 77, 78, 111, 112, 113, 114.

The Illustrated Encyclopedia of Wildlife, Volume 3, pages: 152, 154, 156, 157.

The Little Red Riding Hood by Parragon Books.

The Very Hungry Caterpillar by Eric Carle, Puffin Books.

Quotes:
A remembered quote from Charles Darwin.

A remembered quote from Swami Vivekananda.

Films:
The Lion King by Disney.

Internet:
Tree Article, Wikipedia, pages 1–13.
https://en.wikipedia.org/wiki/Tree.